Violin.

Cavatina

Down Bow. ⊓
Up Bow. V

Larghetto quasi andantino. (♩ = 76.)

JOACHIM RAFF. Op. 85. № 3.

Violin.

Légende.

H. WIENIAWSKI. Op. 17.

Violin.

Violin.
Barcarole.

L. SPOHR. Op. 135.

VIOLIN.
Adagio from Violin Concerto Nº 8.

L. SPOHR. Op. 47.

Violin.
Andante from Violin Concerto.

MENDELSSOHN. Op. 64.

Violin.
Adagio.

MOZART.

Violin.
Romance in G.

L. v. BEETHOVEN. Op. 40.

Violin.
Romance in F.

L. v. BEETHOVEN. Op. 50.

Adagio cantabile. (♩ = 60.)

33013 v

Violin.

poco rall.　　a tempo.

Sul A

restez.

calando.

Fantaisie

ou

SCÈNE DE BALLET

C. de BÉRIOT. Op.100.

Allegro vivace.

Sul D

Recit ad lib.

rall.

Adagio cantabile.

con espress.

ad lib.

Violin.

Violin.

Violin.
Chanson Polonaise.

HENRY WIENIAWSKI. Op. 12.

Violin.
Méditation.

CHARLES GOUNOD.

Andante simplice.

Violin.

Largo.

'Serse'

HANDEL.

Loure.

J.S. BACH.

Ballade.

BERNHARD MOLIQUE.

Andante espressivo.

Adagio and Allegro from Sonata N⁰ 11.

CORELLI.

Violin.
6ᵐᵉ Air Varie.

C. De BERIOT. Op. 12.

INTRODUCTION.
Adagio.

3ᵐᵉ VAR.

4ᵐᵉ VAR.

Maestoso grandioso.

5me VAR.

Allegro con fuoco.

Più lento.

con espress.

Violin.
Air.

BERNHARD MOLIQUE.

Violin.
Aria.

J. S. BACH.

Violin.
Fantasia.

P. RODE. Op. 24.

Allegretto. (♩ = 108.)

p amoroso.

Violin.

Kuyawiak.

Mazurka

HENRY WIENIAWSKI.

Violin.

Polonaise Brillante.

HENRY WIENIAWSKI.

Violin.

Violin.

Bien rhytme et tres largement.

Violin.
Scherzino.

JOACHIM RAFF. Op. 85 № 4.

Violin.

Air Varié.

P. RODE. Op.16.

Violin.

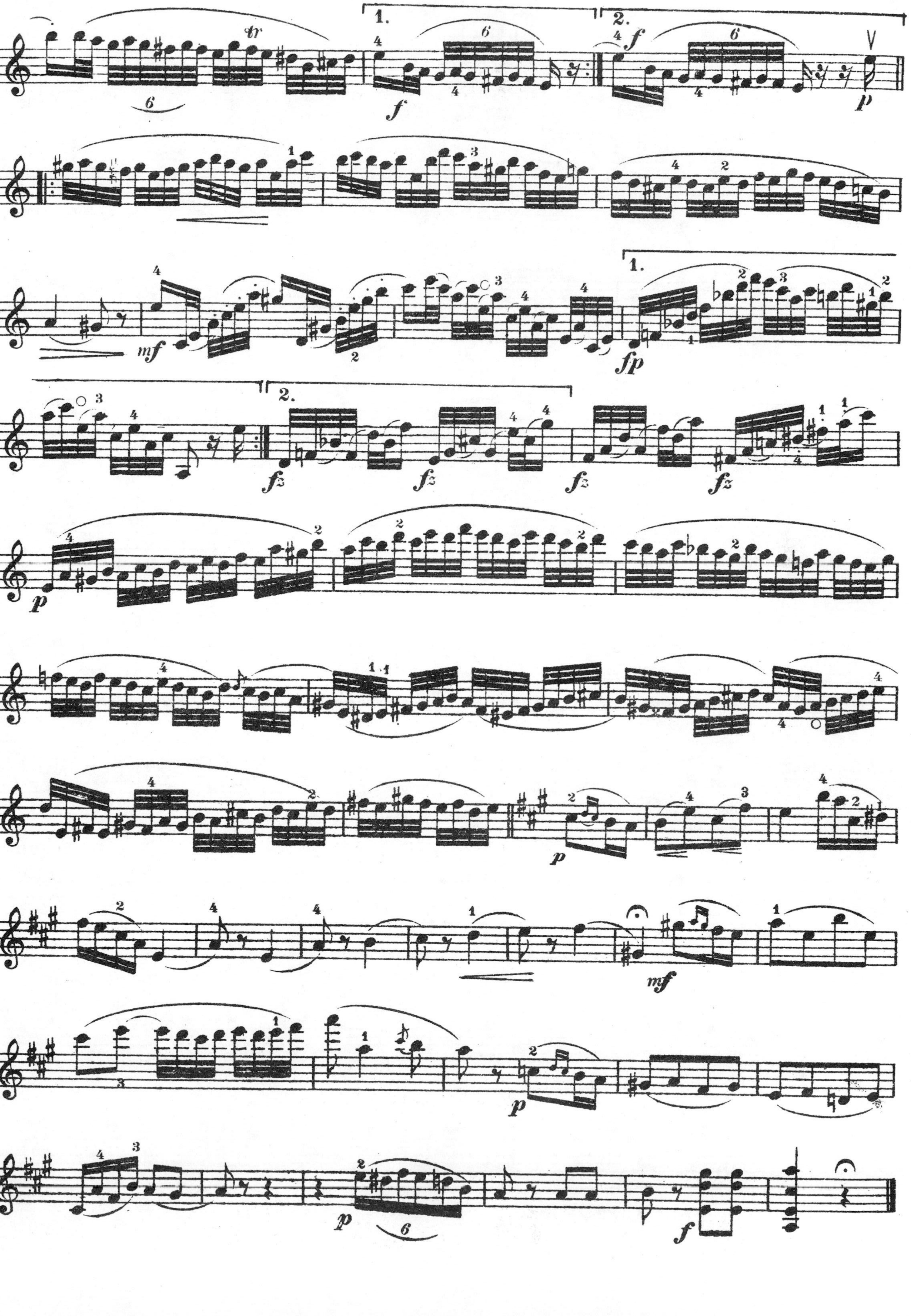

Violin.
Rêverie.

HENRY VIEUXTEMPS. Op. 22. No 3.

Air Varié.

P. RODE. Op. 10.

VAR. 4.

Tempo primo.

con forza.

restez.

p

f

⌐1. ⌐2.

p

calando.

pp